Peter Maxwell Davies

Prayer of Thanksgiving
in Times of Terror

for SATB Chorus and Organ
[2005]

ED 12900

SCHOTT

Mainz · London · Madrid · New York · Paris · Prag · Tokyo · Toronto

PETER MAXWELL DAVIES

Prayer of Thanksgiving in Times of Terror

for SATB Chorus and Organ

[2005]

ED 12900

Commissioned by The Chapel Royal, St. James's Palace to mark the four hundredth anniversary of the Gunpowder Plot in November, 1605

First performance: 5 November 2005
                        Chapel Royal St. James's
                        Andrew Grant, Choirmaster
                        Waltham Abbey
                        Essex

For SATB Chorus and Organ

Duration: 7 minutes

Text

The text is adapted from a speech by the Earl of Northampton, Commissioner at the trial of Henry Garnet for High Treason, as a Gunpowder Plot conspirator, at the Guild-Hall, London in 1606.

Quid facit in pectore humano
Lupi feritas?
Canis rabies?
Serpentis venenum?

Your charter was to destroy
Without sound & due repentance,
Which,
By merit of Christ's Passion
Will serve
In quacunque hora peccator ingemuerit:
Your charter was to destroy:
Such was your burning charity.

Yet peace is the mark whereat the Holy Ghost
Would have all to aim:
It is the razor that cuts the throat of crying sin:
It is the good angel that drives horror out of the
                                    conscience of everyone,
Even when Death threatens.
It is both the richest & the last jewel which,
Departing hence to His Father,
He left to us for a legacy.
And therefore our payer must be thus:

Nulla salus bello,
Pacem te poscimus omnes.

for the Choir of the Chapel Royal, St. James'

PRAYER OF THANKSGIVING IN TIME OF TERROR

Peter Maxwell Davies

© 2005 Schott & Co. Ltd, London

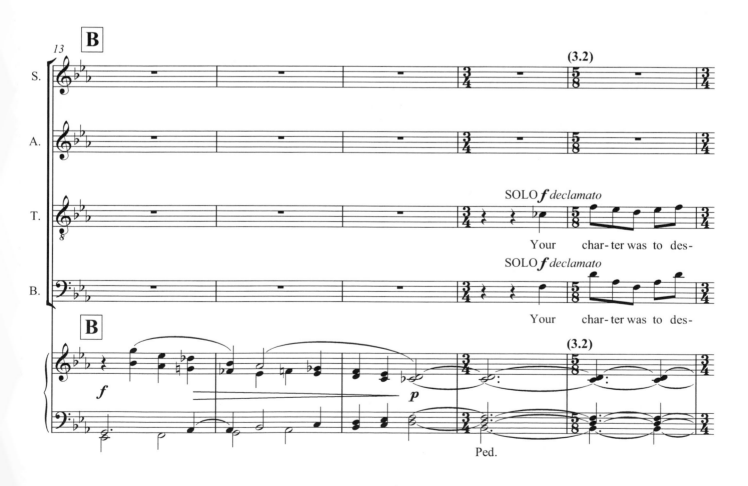

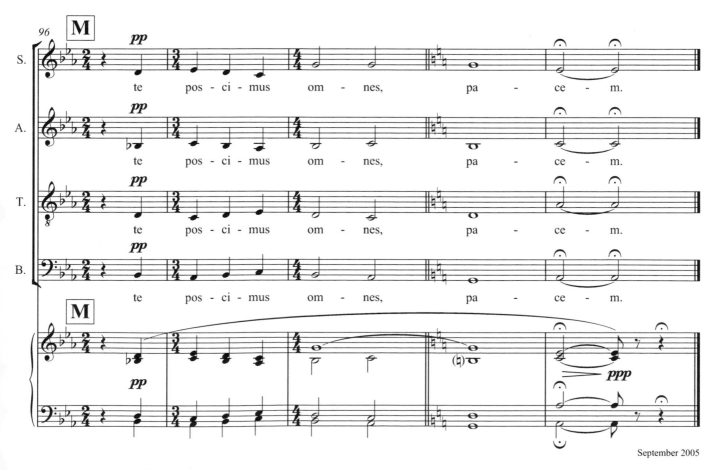

September 2005

ISMN M-2201-2468-6   ED 12900